Sam wants to go out.

What a day!

2

Sam is fed up.

She does not want to play.

She does not want to cook.

She does not want to paint.

Bang! Flash!

8

Everything goes off.

It is dark and cold.

Dad gets some candles.

Mum gets a book.

They all get into bed.

Sam wants to stay in!